THE Lettering Workbook

FOR LARGE TIP

Brush Pen

A Simple Guide To
Hand Lettering & Modern Calligraphy

RICCA'S GARDEN

Think you need more practice?

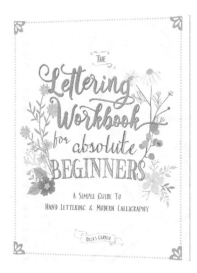

THE LETTERING WORKBOOK FOR ABSOLUTE BEGINNERS

If you're a beginner who's absolutely determined to learn the art of hand lettering but don't know where to start, this workbook is for you!

- Learn multiple lettering styles easily! Covered in this book will be the clssic brush lettering, monoline, faux calligraphy, san serif and serif
- Draw embellishments and design your own artworks using easy-to-understand instructions
- Download ALL the practice pages you need from the workbook to refine your technique and come out a better hand-letterer — for FREE

And so much more!

Check out this workbook here!

THE LETTERING WORKBOOK FOR SMALL TIP BRUSH PEN

Express yourself freely as you learn the beautiful strokes with a small tip brush pen! Whether you are a brush lettering beginner or not, this guide will introduce and help you practice with easy-to understand instructions. You will find:

- The basic brush lettering alphabet, broken down into individual strokes to assist learning
- The bouncy and flourishing lettering styles to perfect your designs for different occasions
- A week of appreciation challenge to follow and inspire you on your lettering journey

As always, ALL the practice pages from the workbook will be available for download!

Check out this workbook here!

ⓘ ricca_garden

✉ info@riccagarden.com

Published & Designed in Brisbane, Australia

First print: Dec 2022

Hello Hand Letterer!

If you are anything like me, once you start lettering, it is tempting to try out every tool you see. You do not need a lot of fancy brush pens to get started. However, you are likely to have come across brush pens with a range of tip sizes.

The tip size you choose will determine the scale of your lettering; hence when it comes to practice, you will also need a workbook that is scaled specifically for your brush pens.

As you have picked up this workbook, I believe you are ready to create bolder designs with a large tip brush pen. To build a strong foundation, we will start by practicing the basic strokes before we move on to drawing the alphabet. We will also have a go at special techniques like ribbon and 3D lettering, so your design can stand out from the page. This guide has plenty of tips and tricks to support you, and I know you want to get started. So, let's begin!

Your lettering skill will excel with lots of practice, so be sure to download the practice sheets by scanning the QR code above or by visiting: https://riccagarden.com/large-tip-lettering/.

Table of Contents

Getting Started with Brush Lettering

IIf you are looking to create hand lettering that is bolder and more dramatic, then using a large tip brush pen may be your best bet! This guide is a useful and fun way to set you up with the basics.

Large tip brush pens are often seen as more challenging for beginners because they generally have a softer tip, making them harder to control. The main challenges you may face while using large tip pens are getting used to writing bigger letters and making consistent thin upstrokes. That is why it is crucial to use practice sheets specifically designed for large tip brush pens, which you'll receive with this guide.

Having said all of this, don't be discouraged! Just have fun while you practice.

Myths about Lettering

Before you start practicing, let's debunk some common hand lettering myths:

My handwriting is not that great. Can I still become a good hand letterer?

Of course, you can! In our everyday handwriting, we might not pay much attention to each letter we are writing, especially when we are just trying to jot down some quick notes. However, when we are hand lettering, we learn to take our time to draw each stroke intentionally and thoughtfully. So even if your handwriting isn't the best, you can still be a good hand letterer.

Isn't cursive writing and hand lettering the same thing?

Many people think cursive writing and hand lettering are the same, but they are not. Although they may seem identical, you wouldn't normally pause or lift your pen between each letter when writing in cursive. Instead, hand lettering is created with a set of basic strokes that requires you to lift your pen from time to time. Lifting your pen gives you a better grip and more control over the brush pen.

I am lettering too slowly!

There is a misconception that you need to hand letter at the same speed as your everyday handwriting. Many things come into play when you are lettering. For example, you need to add different pressure to the brush pen to create thin and thick strokes and pay attention to the spacing and consistency of the letters. If you are lettering too fast, the lines can get shaky, so there is no need to worry about your speed! Work at a pace that is enjoyable to you.

The tools that I need for hand lettering are expensive.

Yes, some pens can be expensive and add up to a considerable amount if you want to try them all. However, you don't need the most expensive tools or the tools professionals use to produce better hand lettering. The way your hand lettering develops is about practicing! There are so many affordable brush pens that can help you create great results. You can even start practicing with just a pencil or Crayola marker!

Let's learn more about the brush pens that can be used with this guide.

Brush Pens

Tombow Dual Tip Brush Pen

Ease of control: ★★★☆☆

Tip Flexibility： ★★★★☆

With over 100 colors to select from, the Tombow Dual Brush Pen is very popular, with good reason. It is a double-ended water-based marker with a brush tip on one end and a bullet tip on the other. The brush tip is large and flexible, so it takes beginners a little while to get used to it. The bullet tip is ideal for monoline lettering and drawing embellishment.

Kuretake Zig Fudebiyori Brush Pen

Ease of control: ★★★★☆

Tip Flexibility： ★★★☆☆

Fudebiyori is a great beginner pen. It comes with a fairly firm tip which makes it easier to control. This pen is smooth and durable and comes in beautiful metallic colors. (This pen has a medium tip, but the practice sheets will suit this pen too!)

Ecoline Watercolor Brush Pen

Ease of control: ★★★☆☆

Tip Flexibility: ★★★★☆

The Ecoline brush pen works well for larger lettering designs as it has the biggest brush tip out of the pens I have suggested here. The watercolor ink is beautiful and juicy, but depending on your paper, you might have to slow down to let the ink dry.

Sakura Koi Coloring Brush Pen

Ease of control: ★☆☆☆☆

Tip Flexibility: ★★★★★

The Sakura Koi brush pens come in a range of vibrant colors. The ink is water-based and can create a beautiful blending effect. However, since the brush tip is soft, a heavy hand letterer may find it slightly harder to control.

Crayola Marker (This is an alternative to the large tip brush pen)

Ease of control: ★★★★☆

Tip Flexibility: ☆☆☆☆☆

The Crayola marker is a perfect practice pen, though it is not a brush pen. You can use it on any paper without worrying that it will fray. Make sure you choose the broad line tip marker because it can create thick and thin strokes when you apply different pressure or change the angle you hold the pen.

Paper

When it comes to lettering, the paper you use is just as important as the brush pen to bring out the best in your work. Although your brush pen will fray eventually, smooth paper can help your pen last longer. Let's explore a few types of paper that can help you on your lettering journey.

Rhodia Paper

The Rhodia paper is a great option for practicing lettering freehand. It comes in various formats and sizes, so you have many options to choose from. The grid or dot format can help your letters stay consistent, and I like to use them to practice my basic strokes.

HP 32 Premium Paper

This HP printer paper is all you need for practice if your budget is limited. It is smooth and holds up ink well compared to regular printer paper. You can print practice sheets on this paper.

TRACING PAPER

The tracing paper is handy when it comes to practice. Since it is translucent, you can place your guide sheet underneath and still be able to see through the page. Moving on to composition, this paper can help you refine your design without starting from scratch.

BRISTOL PAPER

Try Bristol paper if you are looking for something for your final piece. Being a heavyweight paper, it is usually more expensive. Be sure to choose the smooth Bristol paper instead of vellum, which is more textured.

MARKER PAPER

The marker paper is a step up from the tracing paper. It is semi-transparent, so if you place your guide sheets underneath, you can still see it without being too distracted. The paper is thin but smooth, so it will not damage your brush pens.

Position & Posture

In terms of how you sit and hold your brush pen, there are a few things to note. Sit towards the front of the chair, with a straight back and both arms on the table. Your writing hand should just graze the table's edge, not knock into it. Your other arm should rest on the table as a counterbalance.

Hold your brush pen between your thumb and index finger so it sits at a 45° angle to the page. When using a large tip brush pen, beginners tend to have a common problem of holding the pen vertically. However, by doing so, you will not be able to create the full range of line thickness that the brush pen can give you. This might also damage the pen and make it fray quickly, so take note of how you hold it.

As you write, keep your grip fairly loose. Remember that your finger should support the brush pen while your arm does most of the movement. Do not let your hand anchor on the page. Instead, let it glide and move freely to draw smooth lines.

Lettering Tips for Lefties!

Are you unsure if you are holding your tools correctly? Are you worried that the ink will smudge as you write? These are just some common problems that a left-hander may have concerning lettering.

Adapt the usual guidelines but remember that they can be adjusted slightly for practical needs. Try moving your hand above or underneath the words to see which position is the most comfortable for you. Feel free to rotate the paper as you write.

To avoid smearing ink, go slow and place a piece of paper under your hand. Some brush pens dry faster than others, so have fun experimenting with what works for you!

Terminology

There will be lots of terms mentioned throughout the guide, and it may seem overwhelming at first. Don't worry! Always come back and refer to this page.

Baseline	This is the line that all the letters rest on. This line keeps them in place and keeps the letters from slowly creeping further up or down the paper.
Waistline	This is the line where most of the lowercase letters meet at the top (e.g. o, n, a)
Ascender line	This is a higher line, where the tips of taller letters meet (e.g. t, b, l)
Descender line	A line below the baseline. Some lowercase letters have lines that dip and reach the descender line (g, y, p, q).
X-height	This is how tall the lowercase letter x is. It is used to refer to the space between the baseline and the waistline.
Ascender	Any part of a letter that goes above the waistline.
Descender	Any part of a letter that extends past the baseline.
Cross stroke	A horizontal stroke that strikes through letters like t and f.
Flourish	The pretty decorative swirls that are often added as a fancy embellishment to the letters.
Letterform	Basic shape of the letter.

BASIC STROKES & DRILLS

At the start of my lettering journey, I was keen to dive straight into practicing writing letters and words. I skipped over the basic strokes, and as you can imagine, my letters look inconsistent. My lines were shaky, and I did not know which part needed to be thickened. Eventually, I went back to the fundamentals and practiced only the basic strokes. From then on, writing letters came much more naturally because I had already developed muscle memory. So, I strongly encourage you to complete this chapter before moving on!

UPSTROKE

A ─────────────────────────────────

W ─────────────────────────────────

B ─────────────────────────────────

D ─────────────────────────────────

(Shaky lines, lines are too thick, uneven pressure)

You'll apply the least pressure to create a thin upstroke. Start from the baseline and end at the waistline to begin with. Once you get used to that, practice drawing your upstrokes from the baseline to the ascender line. What you're looking for is a consistent thin line. However, remember that you are using a large tip pen, so it is natural that you cannot create strokes that are as thin as they would be with a small tip pen. For extra exercise, use grid paper to practice your upstrokes, starting from one square, then two, then three.

DOWNSTROKE

A ——————————————————————

W ——————————————————————

B ——————————————————————

D ——————————————————————

A ——————————————————————

W ——————————————————————

B ——————————————————————

D ——————————————————————

(Inconsistent pressure)

Downstrokes are the reverse of upstrokes as they are thicker lines that need more pressure applied. Remember to hold your pen at an angle so the lines can be thickened. The more you tilt your pen, the thicker the downstroke will be. Start with a shorter downstroke from the waist to the baseline. Make sure you apply equal pressure, so the line has a consistent thickness. Then, move on to practicing your downstroke from the ascender line to the baseline.

W ——————————————————————

B ——————————————————————

W ——————————————————————

B ——————————————————————

A ——————————————————————

W ——————————————————————

B ——————————————————————

A ——————————————————————

W ——————————————————————

B ——————————————————————

Underturn

A ————————————   A ————————————   A ————————————

W ————————————   W ————————————   W ————————————

B ————————————   B ————————————   B ————————————

D ————————————   D ————————————   D ————————————

(Too narrow at the bottom, not releasing pressure at the right time, the lines are not parallel)

Underturns can be found in letters like a, d, and i. For a small underturn, start from the waistline and release pressure about 2/3 down. Let your line get thinner as you curve up into an upstroke. Make bigger underturns from the ascender line to the baseline. Practice creating equal curves in your underturns, keeping your lines parallel. Underturn is probably one of the strokes that many people struggle with. It takes practice to create a clean transition between thick to thin lines. Use grid paper or print out practice sheets with this guide for more exercise.

Overturn

A ———————

W ———— 1 🡕 𝓷 ⌒ 2 ↘

B ———————

A ———————

W ———— 𝓷 𝓷

B ———————

D ———————

A ———————

W ———— 𝓷 𝓷

B ———————

D ———————

(The lines are not parallel, not enough contrast between thick & thin strokes)

Overturns are in letters like m and n. They are the reverse of underturns. This time, start an upstroke from the baseline and curve at the waistline into a downstroke. Make sure your overturn has enough contrast between thick and thin strokes. Also, keep the lines parallel!

W ——————————————————————

B ——————————————————————

W ——————————————————————

B ——————————————————————

A ——————————————————————

W ——————————————————————

B ——————————————————————

A ——————————————————————

W ——————————————————————

B ——————————————————————

COMPOUND CURVE

A ————————————— A —————————————

W ————————————— W ————————————— W —————————————

B ————————————— B ————————————— B —————————————

D ————————————— D ————————————— D —————————————

A compound curve combines overturn and underturn, drawn in one stroke. Start from the baseline, draw a thin upstroke, curve back down into a thick downstroke, then repeat an upstroke. Use the space between the base and the ascender line to practice bigger compound curves. These strokes can be found in letters like h, m, and n and when connecting letters.

OVAL

A

W

B

D

(The oval is not closed, applying pressure too late, no clear variation in the line weight)

An oval is an elongated circle commonly seen in letters like a, g, d, and o. Start from the top right just below the waistline and curve anticlockwise into a downstroke. Start releasing pressure about 1/3 away from the baseline and curve up to your starting point with light pressure. The oval allows you to practice applying and releasing pressure to create enough line variation.

ASCENDING LOOP

A ———— 2 ———— A ———————— A ————————
W ———————— W ———————— W ————————
B ———————— B ———————— B ————————
D ———————— D ———————— D ————————

(Applying pressure too late, the loop is too
small, no clear variation in the line weight)

Look out for ascending loops in letters like h, b, and d. Start a curved upstroke from the waistline and curve anticlockwise at the ascender line. Add pressure into the downstroke and make sure it joins with your starting point. Try to keep your loops consistent.

A ————————————————————————
W ————————————————————————
B ————————————————————————

A ————————————————————————
W ————————————————————————
B ————————————————————————

A ————————————————————————
W ————————————————————————
B ————————————————————————

DESCENDING LOOP

A

W

B

2   1

D

A

W

B

D

A

W

B

D

(Releasing pressure too early, the loop is too small, no clear variation in the line weight)

Found in letters like g and y, the descending loop is the reverse of the ascending loop. Start from the waistline, draw a downstroke and release pressure at the descender line. Rise into a loop with a thin upstroke and finish at the baseline. The loop of this stroke is always on the left except for the letter q, which is on the right.

W

B

D

W

B

D

W

B

D

ADDITIONAL DRILLS

Here are some additional drills to practice. You may notice we're almost writing complete letterforms! Let's have a go! This first drill involves a slanted upstroke and a downstroke. Remember to lift your pen between strokes and practice how you control your pen with less pressure on your upstrokes and more pressure on your downstrokes.

This drill is a series of three connected underturns. This time you'll be developing how to transition between thick and thin lines. Try to create equally spaced curves.

For connected underturns, practice transitioning between thick and thin strokes, as in the previous example.

Next, try connecting your ovals with small upstrokes in between. Make sure your ovals are closed and try to make them look the same.

Although it seems like a series of compound curves can be connected without lifting the pen, pause anyway as it will help you gain more control over the brush pen. Start your compound curve as normal and lift your pen in your second upstroke halfway between the waist and the baseline. Continue and try to connect your next compound curve seamlessly.

W

B
W

B

This next drill is great for setting you up for letters like b and h. Start from the baseline with an upstroke and lift your pen at the waistline. Add an ascending loop. Repeat and check for consistency.

A

W

B
A

W

B

This time, try adding the upstroke to a descending loop, which you may find in the letter j.

A

W

B
A

W

B

Everything we have covered so far forms the foundation of brush lettering. You can always come back to this chapter to warm up your muscles before each practice session.

PRACTICE HERE!

THE ALPHABET

Now that we have covered the basic strokes and drills, we can move on to the alphabet! Remember to be patient with yourself when you are just starting with a large tip pen. It may take longer to make smooth transitions between thick and thin lines. Nevertheless, it's all part of the fun, so let's begin!

Lowercase Alphabet

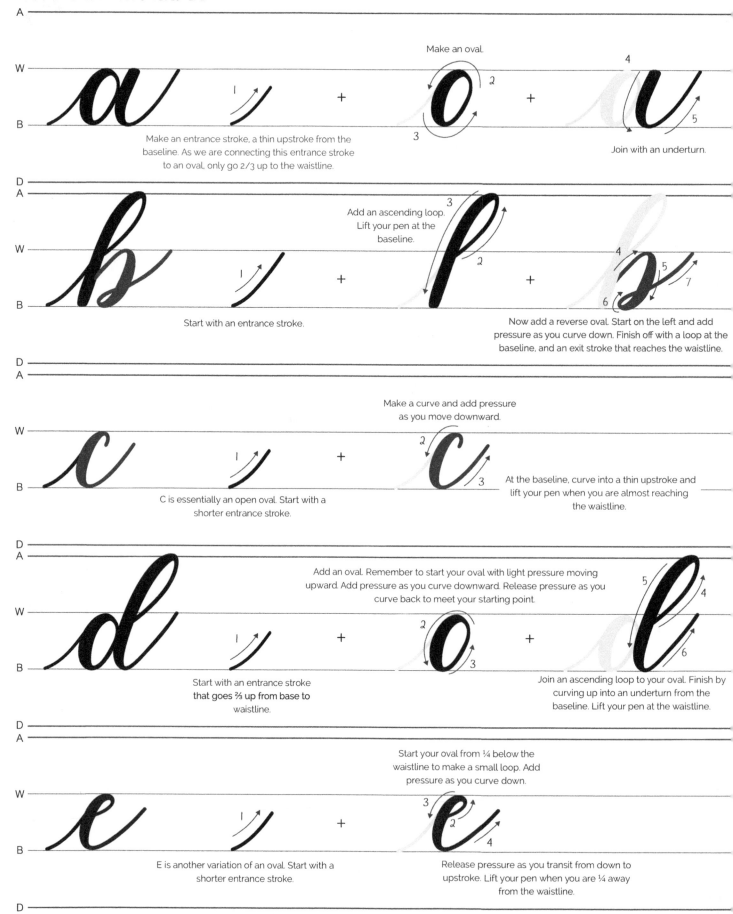

a

Make an entrance stroke, a thin upstroke from the baseline. As we are connecting this entrance stroke to an oval, only go 2/3 up to the waistline.

Make an oval.

Join with an underturn.

b

Start with an entrance stroke.

Add an ascending loop. Lift your pen at the baseline.

Now add a reverse oval. Start on the left and add pressure as you curve down. Finish off with a loop at the baseline, and an exit stroke that reaches the waistline.

c

C is essentially an open oval. Start with a shorter entrance stroke.

Make a curve and add pressure as you move downward.

At the baseline, curve into a thin upstroke and lift your pen when you are almost reaching the waistline.

d

Start with an entrance stroke that goes ⅔ up from base to waistline.

Add an oval. Remember to start your oval with light pressure moving upward. Add pressure as you curve downward. Release pressure as you curve back to meet your starting point.

Join an ascending loop to your oval. Finish by curving up into an underturn from the baseline. Lift your pen at the waistline.

e

E is another variation of an oval. Start with a shorter entrance stroke.

Start your oval from ¼ below the waistline to make a small loop. Add pressure as you curve down.

Release pressure as you transit from down to upstroke. Lift your pen when you are ¼ away from the waistline.

a a a

b b b

c c c

d d d

e e e

Lowercase Alphabet

f

Draw an entrance stroke.

Make an ascending loop that passes the baseline.

When you reach ⅔ beneath the baseline, release pressure as you curve anticlockwise at the descender line. Finish your loop at the baseline and lift your pen.

Add a **final** exit stroke.

g

Start with an entrance stroke that goes ⅔ up from base to waistline.

Make an oval.

Add a descending loop. Always check the interior spacing of your ovals and loops. Try to keep them consistent.

Add an exit stroke.

h

Make an entrance stroke.

Add an ascending loop that **finishes** at the baseline.

Add a compound curve from the baseline.

i

I may be the easiest letter to learn. Make an entrance stroke.

Add an underturn.

Finish your I with a dot.

j

Make an entrance stroke.

Add a descending loop.

Add a **final** upstroke from the baseline as an exit stroke.

Finish off with a dot on the descending loop.

f f f

g g g

h h h

i i i

j j j

Lowercase Alphabet

Start with an entrance stroke.

Add an ascending loop.

Make a small loop and add an underturn. Finish just below the waistline.

After your entrance stroke, attach an ascending loop.

Transition to an underturn when you pass the waistline.

Add another overturn that connects to the first one.

Make an overturn. Lift your pen at the baseline.

Finish with a compound curve, lift pen at the waistline. Remember to keep the strokes parallel and evenly spaced.

Once you get used to the letter m, n is very easy. N is similar to m, only you make one overturn, then a compound curve.

Create an oval.

Make an entrance stroke.

To finish, add a small curved horizontal line at the top of your oval. This horizontal line functions to connect to the next letter.

k k k

l l l

m m m m

n n n n

o o o

Lowercase Alphabet

p — Make a reverse oval, starting from ¼ beneath the waistline. Curve clockwise and add pressure as you move down. Instead of finishing your oval, make a small loop at the baseline and strike through the oval with an exit stroke.

Make an entrance stroke. + Add a descending loop. +

q — Add a descending loop. This time, the descending loop will face the right.

Draw an entrance stroke and finish about ⅔ up from the baseline. + Add an oval. + Add an exit stroke from base to waistline.

r — Make a small loop going anticlockwise just above the waistline.

Make an entrance stroke from base to waistline. + Transition to an underturn.

s — Make a small loop on the waistline and curve anticlockwise. Make an S shape with a downstroke. Curve clockwise at the baseline and strike through the S with an exit stroke.

S is a unique letter that requires you to draw a variation of the basic stroke. Make an entrance stroke. +

t — Draw an entrance stroke. + Add a downstroke, then release pressure ⅔ below the waistline as you transition to an underturn. + Finish with a cross stroke.

LOWERCASE ALPHABET

A

W

Add two underturns. Lift pen at the waistline each time.

B

Make an upstroke.

D
A

Make a compound curve. As you finish your final upstroke, loop at the waistline. The final loop is the stroke that connects to the following letter.

D
A

W

Add an underturn.

B

Make an entrance stroke.

Add your second underturn and make a loop at the waistline.

D
A

Strike through the middle downstroke with a thin diagonal upstroke that slightly curves at the ends.

W

B

Make a compound curve. Practice keeping the up and downstroke parallel.

D
A

Add a descending loop.

Add an exit stroke from where the loop finishes.

W

B

Make a compound curve.

D

u u u

v v v

w w w

x x x

y y y

LOWERCASE ALPHABET

A

W

Make an overturn.

B

At the bottom of your overturn, start a reversed
oval, making a thicker downstroke as you graze
the descender line and curve back up.

+

Strike through the upper part of the
oval with an upstroke.

D
A

W

B

D
A

W

B

D
A

W

B

D
A

W

B

D
A

W

B

D

Uppercase Alphabet

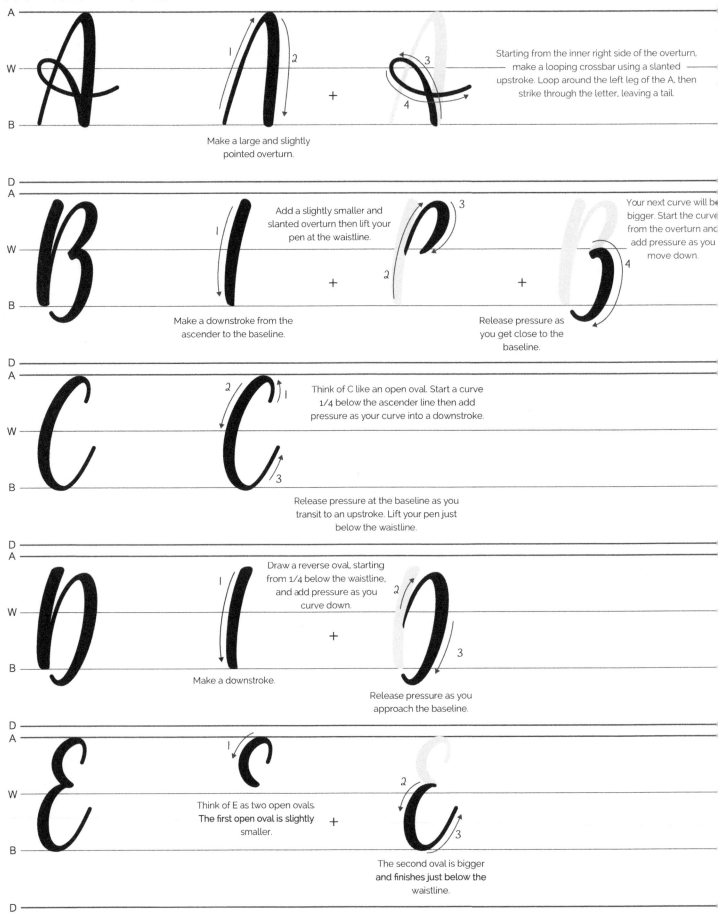

A

Make a large and slightly pointed overturn.

Starting from the inner right side of the overturn, make a looping crossbar using a slanted upstroke. Loop around the left leg of the A, then strike through the letter, leaving a tail.

B

Make a downstroke from the ascender to the baseline.

Add a slightly smaller and slanted overturn then lift your pen at the waistline.

Release pressure as you get close to the baseline.

Your next curve will be bigger. Start the curve from the overturn and add pressure as you move down.

C

Think of C like an open oval. Start a curve 1/4 below the ascender line then add pressure as your curve into a downstroke.

Release pressure at the baseline as you transit to an upstroke. Lift your pen just below the waistline.

D

Make a downstroke.

Draw a reverse oval, starting from 1/4 below the waistline, and add pressure as you curve down.

Release pressure as you approach the baseline.

E

Think of E as two open ovals. **The first open oval is slightly** smaller.

The second oval is bigger **and finishes just below the** waistline.

A A A

B B B

C C C

D D D

E E E

Make a downstroke.

Add a curvy cross stroke that sits on top of the downstroke.

Add a shorter cross stroke that strikes through the stem.

Make a large open oval, just like an uppercase C.

Add a descending loop and strike through the stem, leaving a tail.

Make a descending loop from the ascender to the baseline. Then, as you curve up, strike through the stem and connect it to an ascending loop.

Finish your downstroke by curving up into an underturn. Lift your pen just below the waistline.

I is simple. Just make a downstroke!

Add a slanted upstroke.

Make a descending loop. As you curve up, loop through the stem, leaving a tail.

Uppercase Alphabet

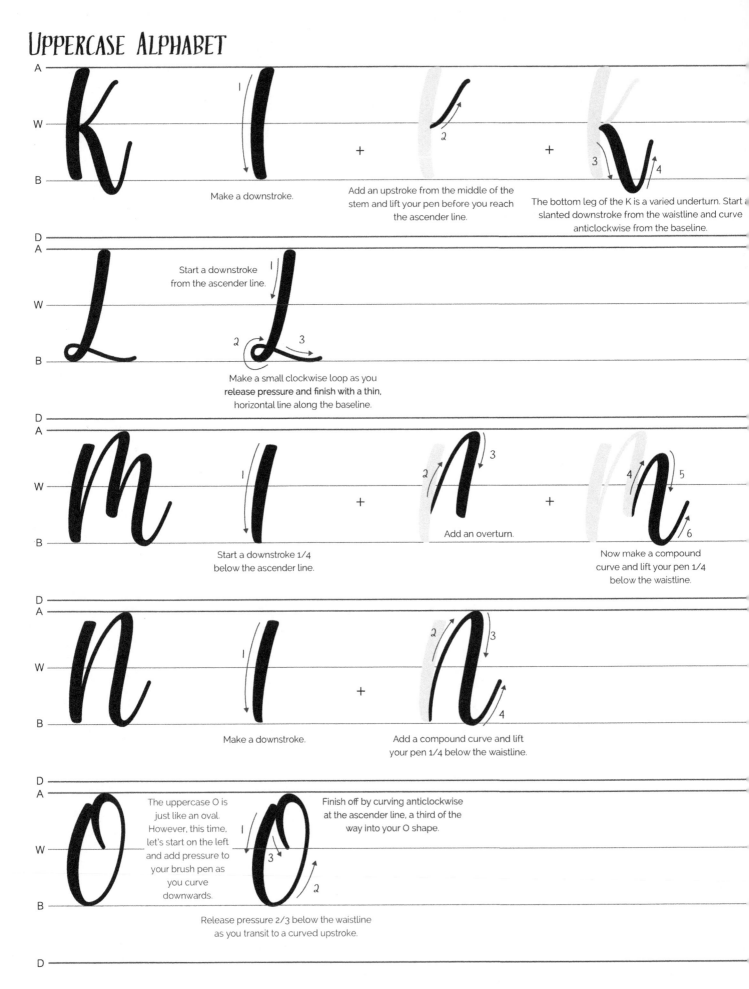

Make a downstroke.

Add an upstroke from the middle of the stem and lift your pen before you reach the ascender line.

The bottom leg of the K is a varied underturn. Start a slanted downstroke from the waistline and curve anticlockwise from the baseline.

Start a downstroke from the ascender line.

Make a small clockwise loop as you release pressure and finish with a thin, horizontal line along the baseline.

Start a downstroke 1/4 below the ascender line.

Add an overturn.

Now make a compound curve and lift your pen 1/4 below the waistline.

Make a downstroke.

Add a compound curve and lift your pen 1/4 below the waistline.

The uppercase O is just like an oval. However, this time, let's start on the left and add pressure to your brush pen as you curve downwards.

Finish off by curving anticlockwise at the ascender line, a third of the way into your O shape.

Release pressure 2/3 below the waistline as you transit to a curved upstroke.

K K K

L L L

M M M

N N N

O O O

Uppercase Alphabet

P

| 1 | + | 2 P 3 | Add a reverse oval starting from the middle of the stem. |

Make a downstroke.

Release pressure as you meet the stem below the waistline to finish.

Q

Q is another oval variation. Start with an upstroke between the waist and baseline.

Curve clockwise at the ascender line, and remember to add pressure to your downstroke.

Release pressure at the baseline to make a small clockwise loop.

R

| 1 | + | 2 P 3 | + | R 4 |

Make a downstroke.

Add a reverse oval starting from the middle of the stem and lift your pen at the waistline.

Add a slanted downstroke to make the leg of the R shape.

S

Start the S just like drawing a loose oval. When you reach the waistline, continue to curve down with pressure.

The tail at the end can function as a connecting stroke.

Finish the S shape by releasing pressure at the baseline as your curve clockwise into a loop.

T

| 1 | + | 2 T |

Make a downstroke.

Add a crossbar on top.

P P P

Q Q Q

R R R

S S S

T T T

Uppercase Alphabet

Make a large underturn.

Add another underturn. This time lift your pen just below the waistline.

The V is simply a pointed underturn.

Make a big underturn but lift your pen just above the waistline.

Add another underturn and lift your pen at the ascender line.

Make a slanted underturn but lift your pen just below the waistline.

Strike through the middle of the stem with a diagonal upstroke from the base to the ascender line.

Add a descending loop.

Make an underturn.

Strike through the stem, leaving a tail.

U U U

V V V

W W W

X X X

Y Y Y

A

W

B

$\mathcal{Z}$

D

The Z begins with a varied overturn. Start
your upstroke on the waistline, and
add pressure as you curve back down.

+

Strike through the bottom
curve and lift your pen.

Join a reverse oval and release
pressure as you loop back up.

A

W

B

D
A

W

B

D
A

W

B

D
A

W

B

D
A

W

B

D

$\mathcal{Z}$ $\mathcal{Z}$ $\mathcal{Z}$

PRACTICE NUMBERS TOO!

1 2 3 4 5 6 7 8 9 0

1 2 3 4 5 6 7 8 9 0

1 2 3 4 5 6 7 8 9 0

Connecting Letters

Hopefully, you are nice and warmed up after all of the basic strokes and alphabet practice. We can now take the next step towards writing words by connecting letters. Here are a few things to note:

1. The way you connect your letters should be consistent throughout your text.

See the example "shine" below. Note how the connecting curves are similar in length, weight, and shape. You also want to keep the spacing between letters consistent.

2. Keep in mind which letters you are writing next.

When you join up the letters, think ahead and know what stroke you are connecting to. For example, if you are connecting to an oval, your exit stroke should not go all the way up to the waistline. If you are connecting an underturn to an overturn, you can make use of the reverse compound curve. This is why picking up your pen in between strokes is important because it gives you time to think about what is ahead.

3. Practice your upstroke (especially when using a large tip pen!)

Many connecting lines involve thin upstrokes. However, by now, you would have noticed that the upstroke is more challenging than it seems. So always go back to the basics and warm up your muscle at the beginning of each practice session.

4. You do not have to connect every letter.

When you add flourish to a letter or start a word with a capital, you don't always need to join it to the rest of the word. Sometimes, leaving the letter separate looks better, so try that too!

The connecting stroke does not have to go up to the waistline when you connect to an oval.

The connecting curves should look consistent.

When you connect i to n you can make use of the reverse compound curve.

pu pu

li li

ku ku

in in

Try using a reverse compound curve to connect the underturn and overturn.

un un

ik ik ik

gh gh gh

nb nb nb

ae ae ae

id id id

CONNECTING LETTERS

mo mo

sh sh

ar ar

ir ir

th th

Try connecting the cross stroke of the t to the ascending loop of h.

look look

path path

mile mile

place place

chill chill

light light

lead lead

hello hello

chocolate

chocolate

Exploring more brush lettering styles

If you are anything like me, I am always looking for new ways to draw the alphabet. I love exploring different brush lettering styles because they can change the mood and feel of the design significantly. Now, we will stretch our muscles and add two more styles to our skill set. Let's dive in!

Sakura

Sakura is a lettering style that makes use of many curves and loops. It carries a more expressive tone, but it is still relatively easy for beginners to learn. Draw your loops slowly so you can get used to transitioning from thin to thick strokes or vice versa.

Aa   Bb   Cc   Dd

Ee   Ff   Gg   Hh

Ji   Jj   Kk   Ll

Mm   Nn   Oo   Pp

Qq   Rr   Ss   Tt

Uu   Vv   Ww   Xx

Yy   Zz

Aa

Bb

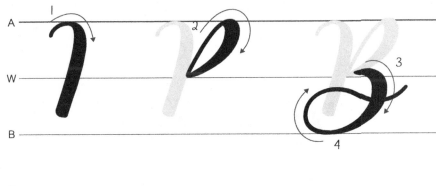

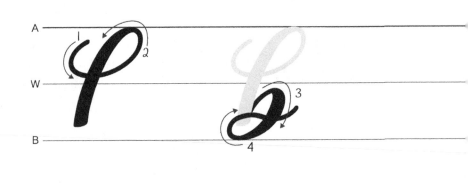

A

W

B

D

A

W

B

D

A

W

B

D

A

W

B

D

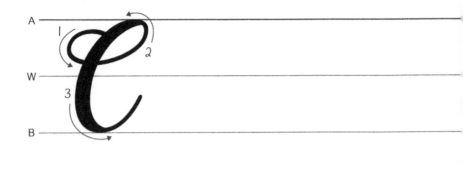

Cc

Dd

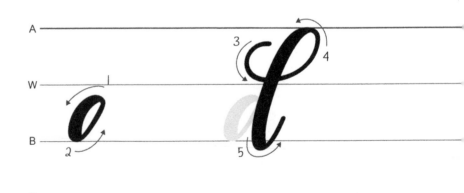

A

W

B

D

A

W

B

D

A

W

B

D

A

W

B

D

E e

F f

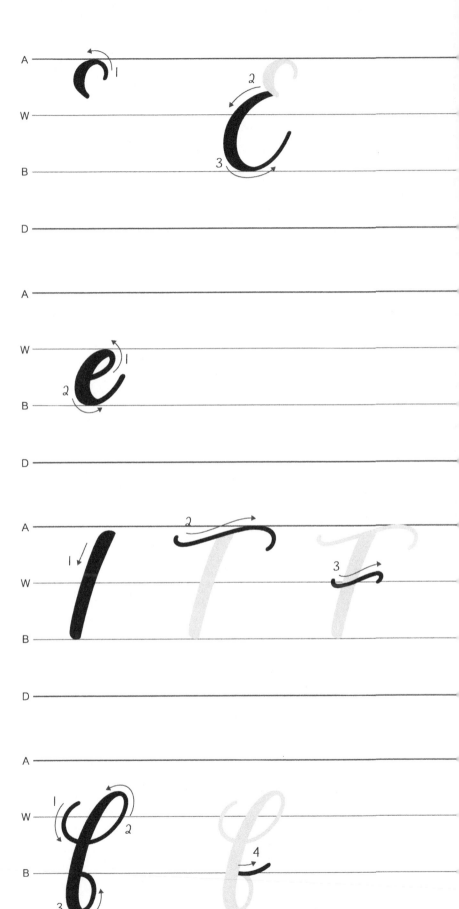

A

W

B

D

A

W

B

D

A

W

B

D

A

W

B

D

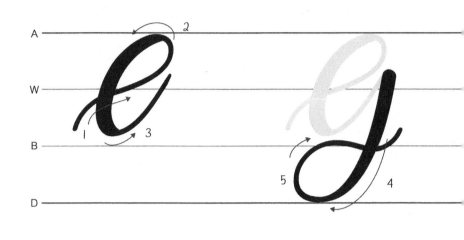

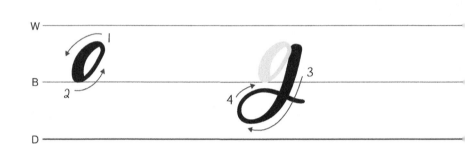

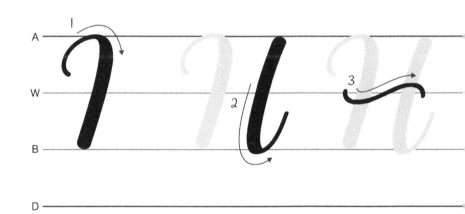

A
W
B
D

Gg Gg Gg

A
W
B
D

Gg

A
W
B
D

Hh Hh Hh

A
W
B
D

Hh

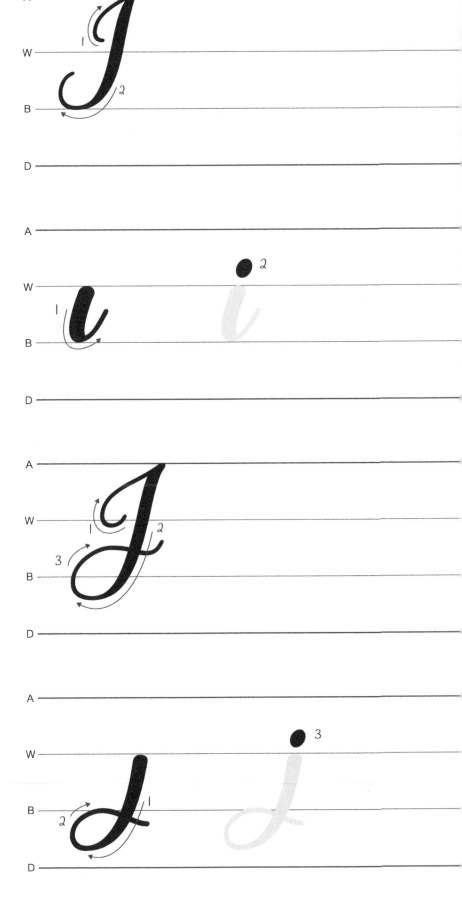

SAKURA

A
Ii Ii Ii
W
B
D

A
Ii
W
B
D

A
Jj Jj Jj
W
B
D

A
Jj
W
B
D

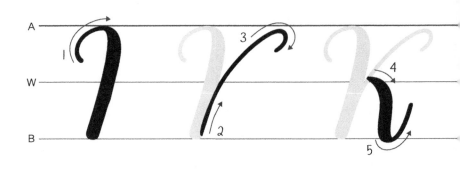

A

W

B

D

A

W

B

D

A

W

B

D

A

W

B

D

Mm

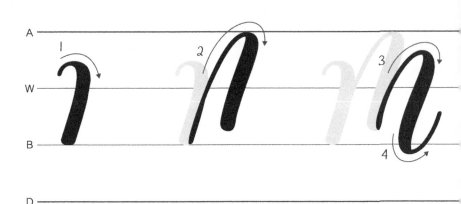

Nn

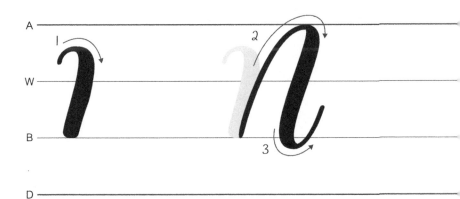

A

W

B

D

Mm Mm Mm

A

W

B

D

Mm

A

W

B

D

Nn Nn Nn

A

W

B

D

Nn

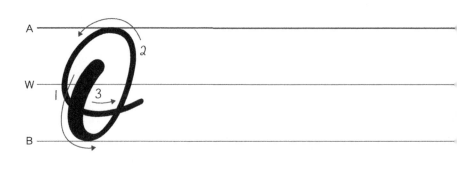

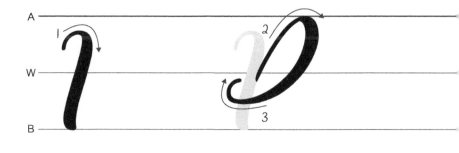

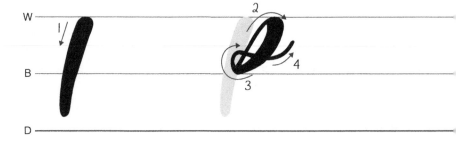

A

W

B

Oo   *Oo*   *Oo*

D

A

W

B

Oo

D

A

W

B

Pp   *Pp*   *Pp*

D

A

W

B

Pp

D

Qq

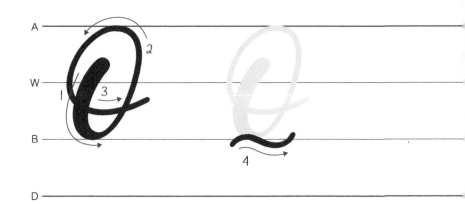

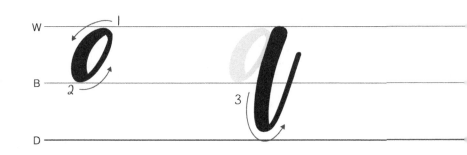

Rr

A

W

B

D

A

W

B

D

A

W

B

D

A

W

B

D

Ss

Tt

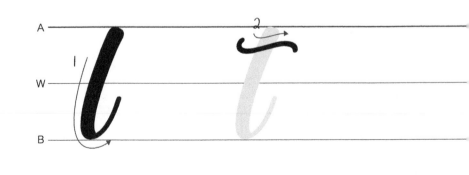

A

W

B

D

A

W

B

D

A

W

B

D

A

W

B

D

Uu

Vv

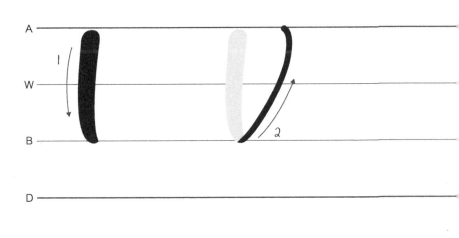

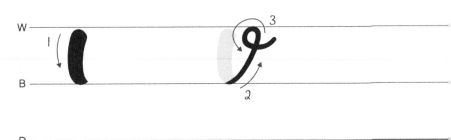

A

W

B

D

Uu   Uu   Uu

A

W

B

D

Uu

A

W

B

D

Vv   Vv   Vv

A

W

B

D

Vv

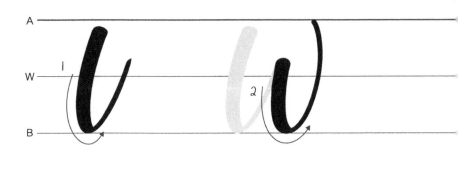

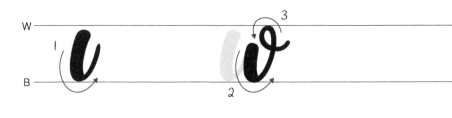

Ww

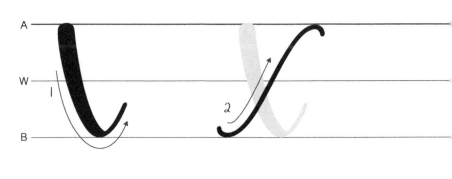

Xx

A

W

B

D

A

W

B

D

A

W

B

D

A

W

B

D

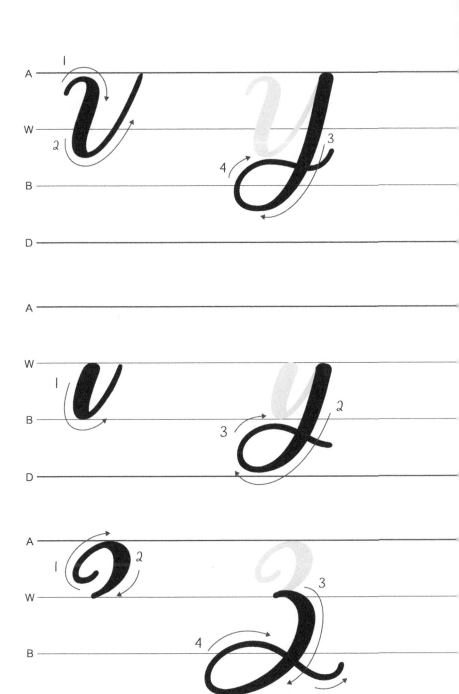

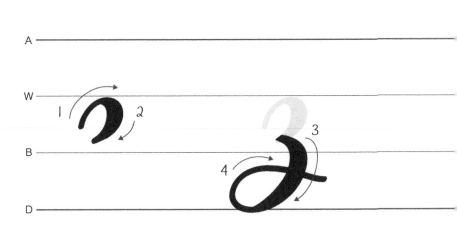

A

W

B

D

A

W

B

D

A

W

B

D

A

W

B

D

Camelia

With its beautiful rhythm, Camelia is a graceful alphabet that will bring your lettering skill to the next level. Don't be intimidated to see its swashes and swirls! With practice, you can also draw elegant letters like this, which look stunning on invitations and greeting cards.

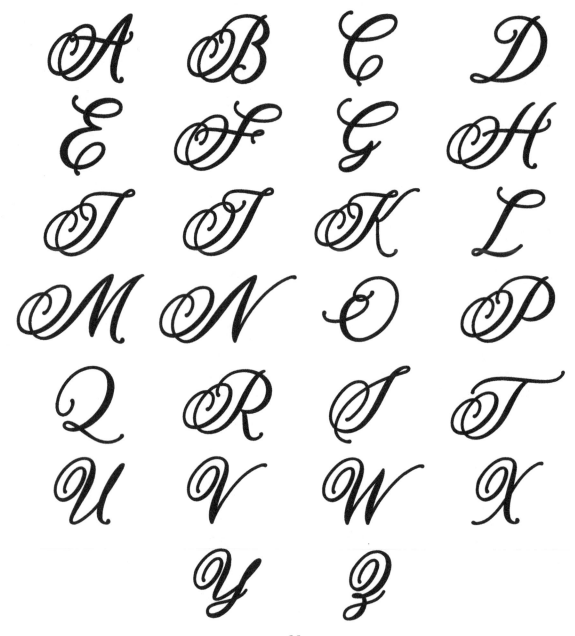

Let's incorporate flourishing when we practice the lowercase alphabet this time. Although it is not the most beginner-friendly decoration, still have fun with them! On the next page, there are some tips to help you get started.

1.   DO NOT PLANT YOUR HAND ON THE PAGE

Use your whole arm to do the movement and try to relax. That way, you will achieve smoother lines.

2.   FLOURISHES ARE BASED ON OVALS

You are essentially stacking and spiraling ovals when you draw flourishes. Keep that in mind so your flourishes can appear natural and graceful.

3.   USE A PENCIL TO SKETCH THE FLOURISHES FIRST BEFORE YOU INK THEM.

Before you get used to drawing the swirling lines, plan ahead with a pencil. You want your flourishes to have room to breathe, and by planning, you can adjust their shape and size.

4.   BE PATIENT WITH YOURSELF!

Don't be discouraged if you don't get the results you want straight away. Flourishes are challenging for many people initially, and you may still be adapting to large tip pens. Just keep going!

Before we start, use the following exercise to practice drawing the flourishes with a pencil. We want to focus on arm movement instead of adding pressure with the brush pen. Once you build muscle memory, flourishes will come more naturally to you.

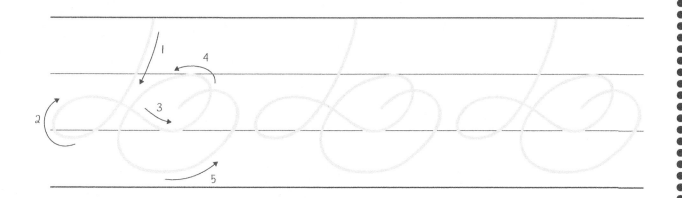

Remember to download the practice sheets online if you need more practice!

A

a

CAMELIA

D   D

1 + 2   3   4

d l   O + l

1   2   4   6   3   5

CAMELIA

CAMELIA

CAMELIA

Same with J, you do not have to separate these two strokes if you feel comfortable drawing them in one.

CAMELIA

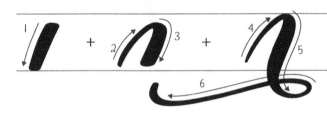

CAMELIA

CAMELIA

CAMELIA

U V (+ (

3 4
1 2 5 6

𝓤

u V + (
1 2 3
5 6 7 4

110

CAMELIA

CAMELIA

$\mathcal{Y}$ $\mathcal{V}$ + $\mathcal{J}$

3   4   6

2   5

1   7

$\mathcal{Y}$ $\mathcal{V}$ + $\mathcal{X}$

1   2   3

6

4   5   7

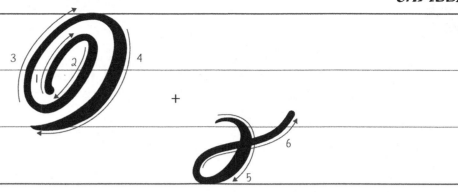

Creating Special Effects

Are you looking for ways to make your lettering stand out even more? In this section, we will explore how to do ribbon and 3D lettering. These are fun ways to add personality to your design!

Ribbon Lettering

Ribbon lettering is a beautiful technique that makes your design leap off the page. Although it may seem complicated at first, with some practice, you will learn it in no time. Here, you would need a brush pen and a fineliner. Grab your tools, and let's get started!

1.   Use a brush pen for lettering a word or phrase. Here, I am using the word "hope" as an example. Normally, we would want our upstrokes to be thin. However, keeping the line weight consistent throughout the word in ribbon lettering is better. That way, there is more space for you to add the details later.

2.   Use a fineliner to draw an outline of the word.

3.   Here is where the fun begins! Imagine how the letters will curve like a ribbon. Some parts will go behind, and some will go in front. As a general rule, the upstrokes will be at the back, and the downstrokes will be at the front. Start drawing the folds.

Use a curve line to create the illusion that the ribbon is folding.

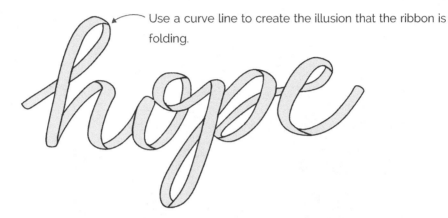

4.   Add depth to your letters using shadow lines. The lines show where the ribbon overlaps each other.

5.   Alternatively, color the upstrokes using a darker shade brush pen to create contrast. Once familiar with the technique, you can also try ribbon lettering without drawing an outline!

3D Lettering

Want to make your letters pop? Try 3D lettering! 3D lettering helps you add another dimension to your design so that the letters can stand out from the page.

1.   Let's use the word "best" in this example.

2.   Decide on the direction you want the 3D effect to be. I will stick to the right side for now. With a pencil, add diagonal lines to the corners. Make sure the lines are all parallel to each other.

3.   Next, we are going to add depth. Draw lines that are parallel to the edge of the letters.

4.   By now, we know where the 3D effect is going to be. We can use a fineliner to ink the outline. Make sure you round the edge of the curves!

5.   To add a twist, enhance the 3D effect with lines.

COMPOSITION

Do you often think you are not creative enough to make a well-composed design? Not to worry, this is how most people feel! However, the blank page does not have to be intimidating. Instead, it can be freeing. Here, I want to show you four ways to compose the quote, "Give Yourself Permission to Slow Down." Remind yourself of the message of the quote too. Creating composition is something you will improve over time so take it slowly!

METHOD 1: FINDING NEGATIVE SPACE

1.   This is probably one of the easiest methods to create a simple layout. Use a pencil to write out the quote in several different ways. Right now, we are just experimenting with the placement of the words, so it does not have to be perfect. Observe how the words align and see if the ascenders or descenders knock into each other.

① *Give yourself permission to slow down*

② *Give yourself permission to slow down*

③ *Give yourself permission to slow down*

2.   The quote looks uneven in the first and third layouts, so let's continue working on the second layout. We will rewrite the quote in the size you want your finished artwork to be. You can use a piece of grid paper underneath as a guide so you do not have a word that slowly creeps up or down the page. After that, mark out the negative spaces. They are the places you can fill up with flourishes to improve the layout.

Give yourself permission to slow down

3.   Decide how you want to extend your letters. It will be best if you still use a pencil at this stage, as you can continue to make changes until you have found your perfect design.

Give yourself permission to slow down

4.   Once satisfied with the design, use a brush pen to ink it. Let it dry completely before you erase the pencil lines. Alternatively, use marker paper to trace over your design.

Give yourself permission to slow down

METHOD 2: HIGHLIGHTING IMPORTANT KEYWORDS

1.   In the second method, we will start by picking out the quotes' important keywords. Here, I would like to emphasize the words "permission" and "slow down".

Give yourself permission to slow down

2.   Again, let's try out different layout ideas. This time we will be writing out the keywords first. Then add in the rest of the words where you see fit. For the non-keywords, you can try using block letters to fill in the space first because it will not have ascenders and descenders that get in the way.

① GIVE YOURSELF
Permission
TO
Slow Down

② GIVE
YOURSELF
Permission
TO
Slow
Down

③ GIVE
yourself
Permission TO
Slow Down

3.   Pick the layout you like best. For now, I would like to work with the third layout. Draw the design again on a new piece of paper, this time in the size you want your final artwork to be. It works best if you are tracing over a grid paper because it will help you align your text. I see some opportunities to extend my letters, so I will go ahead and add some simple flourishes to fill up the space.

GIVE
yourself
Permission to
Slow Down

4.   Now, we are ready to ink the design. If you do not want to go through the tiresome process of erasing afterward, trace over your design using marker paper. Draw the keywords using a brush pen and switch to a monoline marker for block letters.

5.   We have completed the composition in the last step, but I want to make my design look even better. I decided to add some decorative lines to improve the overall look of the layout.

METHOD 3: LETTERING IN BASIC SHAPES

1.   This next method involves planning your quote in basic shapes. As shown in the examples below, you can use shapes like circles, rectangles, or ovals to compose your design.

Divide the shape into sections, so it helps you fit your quote in more easily.

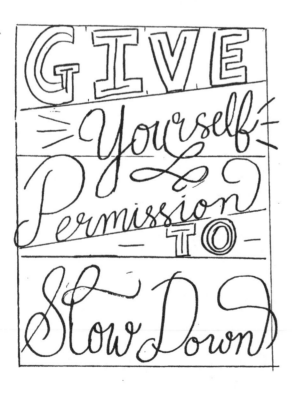

2. Pick your favorite design. I chose to continue working with the oval shape design here. Try to spot some improvements you can make to it. If you do not want to keep erasing your design, grab a new piece of paper and adjust it there. Above the word "permission" there is a space so let's change the word "yourself" to block letters to fill up that area. I have also added some lines to highlight the word "slow".

3. Once you're happy with the new design, you can finish it with the final tools. Again, use a brush pen for the main keywords, and a monoline pen for the block letters and highlights. Erase any pencil marks once the ink has dried.

Method 4: Blocking

1.   Blocking takes the basic shape method to the next step because you will be drawing your quote in a combination of shapes. We will again start by picking out the keywords. In this quote, I would like to highlight the word "permission" this time.

Give yourself permission to slow down

2.   Next, develop a few composition arrangements with shapes like triangles, circles, rectangles, arches, or bridges. Then, think about where you want the keyword to be, and draw that shape bigger. Finally, add some guidelines to help you align your text later.

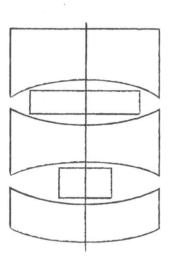
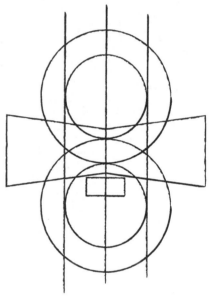

3.   Now try to fit the words in. You can use a combination of lettering styles to create your design.

GIVE *Yourself* PERMISSION TO *Slow* DOWN

4. Choose the composition idea you like the most. The second layout is my pick, so I will use a new piece of paper to trace and redraw the design with my final tools.

GIVE *Yourself* PERMISSION TO *Slow* DOWN

5. Add any embellishments or flourishes you like to perfect your design.

If you ever get stuck on composing your lettering artwork, always come back and revisit the four methods we have gone through in this chapter. Even if your design does not look perfect at the start, it will slowly come together if you keep refining it!

A Week of Self-Care

How are you taking care of yourself in times of stress? Are you finding time to relax and unwind? Hand lettering is a meditative practice that can help you slow down, reflect and center yourself. As you practice lettering positive words and thinking about their messages, it gives you a creative outlet that improves your emotional well-being. Here we have a week of self-care exercises to help you get started.

Every quote is intended to empower you and help you recognize your self-worth. Do not pressure yourself while you practice or focus too much on how well you letter. Instead, use this time to enjoy creating in the present moment. They can be messages you keep for yourself or as gifts for loved ones.

Let's begin!

Day 1: you have always been enough

For day 1, let's start with something simple. Brush lettering the quote and use a marker to draw the teardrop ornaments. I love the message of this quote. Don't strive to be more worthy; you are just enough as you are.

Trace here first.

Now try it yourself.

Day 2: You have the power to be limitless

Today's quote encourages us to believe in our unlimited potential! Draw all the brush letters first before writing the block letters. Make sure your hand can move freely and glide on the page when you draw the flourishes.

Trace here first.

You have the
to be power
limitless

Now try it yourself.

Day 3: let yourself rest

Let's keep today's message short and sweet! Start with the word "yourself" as it is the focal point of this quote. Finish off by adding some decorative lines with a monoline pen to enhance the overall look.

Trace here first.

Now try it yourself.

Day 4: slow progress is still progress

Let today's quote remind you that your productivity will vary daily, which is completely fine! As always, brush letter first and switch to a monoline pen when you draw the rest of the quote. This quote has some big flourishes, so move slowly to maintain control.

Trace here first.

Now try it yourself! You can use a pencil to draw some guidelines to help you.

DAY 5: BE PROUD OF HOW HARD YOU ARE TRYING

Today, take a moment to appreciate yourself for your hard work. At first glance, this quote can look difficult to letter but let's break it down. Draw the main part of the letter first before connecting the flourish to it. Next, try to create a funkier serif style with any stiff marker.

Trace here first.

Now try it yourself! Use a pencil to draw some guidelines to help you.

DAY 6: YOU HAVE DONE YOUR BEST

It's day 6, and we are nearly done with the challenge! As today's quote states, you have done your best! Remember to let your hand glide on the page to get smooth and natural-looking lines.

Trace here first.

Now try it yourself! You can use a pencil to draw some guidelines to help you.

DAY 7: FEEL THE FEAR AND DO IT ANYWAY

We will finish this challenge with a quote to inspire the rest of your creative journey. Don't doubt your abilities to create beautiful artwork! You can master hand lettering with practice. Just put pen to paper!

Trace here first.

Feel the fear but do it Anyway

Now try it yourself.

Congratulations on getting so far in your lettering journey. I hope you are feeling inspired to go forth with more lettering projects. Your confidence will build as you practice, and if you believe in your creative abilities!

Made in the USA
Coppell, TX
02 May 2023

16343194R00077